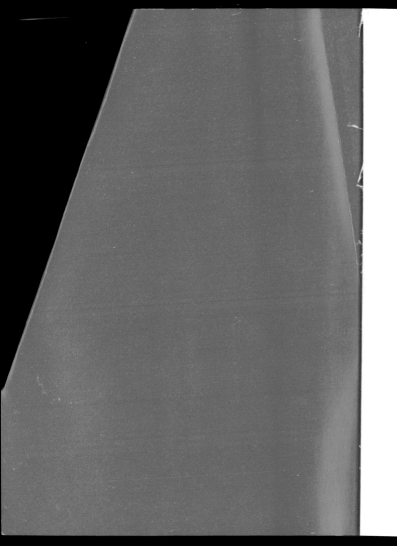

W9-BXA-679

The Silly Littl

KNOC

JOK

The Silly Little Book

of

KNOCK
KNOCK
JOKES

mustard

This edition published and distributed by Mustard, 1999

Mustard is an imprint of Parragon

Parragon
Queen Street House
4–5 Queen Street
Bath BA1 1HE

Produced by Magpie Books, an imprint of
Robinson Publishing Ltd, London

Copyright © Parragon 1999

ISBN 0 75253 007 0

A copy of the British Library Cataloguing-in-Publication Data
is available from the British Library

Printed and bound in Singapore

Contents

Introduction

Don't answer that door! It could be anyone out there, and you'll be in danger of splitting your sides with laughter when "Justine time" or "Amanda the table" comes calling. Check to see if there's a joke for your name and prepare for humor in the hallway and laughter through the letterbox as you leaf through this tremendous selection.

Girls' Names

Knock knock.
Who's there?
Ada.
Ada who?
Ada lot for breakfast.

Knock knock.
Who's there?
Aleta.
Aleta who?
Aleta from your bank manager.

Knock knock.
Who's there?
Alma.
Alma who?
Alma lovin'.

Knock knock.
Who's there?
Althea.
Althea who?
Althea in court.

Knock knock.
Who's there?
Amanda.
Amanda who?
Amanda the table.

Knock knock.
Who's there?
Amber.
Amber who?
Amberter than I was yesterday.

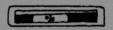

Knock knock.
Who's there?
Amy.
Amy who?
Amy for the top.

Knock knock.
Who's there?
Anna.
Anna who?
Annamazingly good joke.

Knock knock.
Who's there?
Annabel.
Annabel who?
Annabel would be useful on this
door.

Knock knock.
Who's there?
Annette.
Annette who?
Annette curtain looks good in the
window.

Knock knock.
Who's there?
Annie.
Annie who?
Annie one you like.

Knock knock.
Who's there?
Anya.
Anya who?
Anya best behavior.

Knock knock.
Who's there?
Audrey.
Audrey who?
Audrey to pay for this?

Knock knock.
Who's there?
Augusta.
Augusta who?
Augustalmost felt like winter.

Knock knock.
Who's there?
Aurora.
Aurora who?
Aurora's just come from a big lion!

Knock knock.
Who's there?
Ava.
Ava who?
Ava good mind to leave you.

Knock knock.
Who's there?
Barbara.
Barbara who?
(sing) "Barbara black sheep, have
you any wool?"

Knock knock.
Who's there?
Barbie.
Barbie who?
Barbie Q.

Knock knock.
Who's there?
Bea.
Bea who?
Bea love and open the door.

Knock knock.
Who's there?
Bella.
Bella who?
Bella the ball.

Knock knock.
Who's there?
Bernadette.
Bernadette who?
Bernadette my dinner.

Knock knock.
Who's there?
Beth.
Beth who?
Beth foot forward.

Knock knock.
Who's there?
Bethany.
Bethany who?
Bethany good shows recently?

Knock knock.
Who's there?
Bette.
Bette who?
Bette of roses.

Knock knock.
Who's there?
Bettina.
Bettina who?
Bettina minute you'll go to sleep.

Knock knock.
Who's there?
Betty.
Betty who?
Betty earns a lot of money.

Knock knock.
Who's there?
Bridget.
Bridget who?
Bridget on the River Kwai.

Knock knock.
Who's there?
Bridie.
Bridie who?
Bridie light of the silvery moon.

Knock knock.
Who's there?
Caitlin.
Caitlin who?
Caitlin you my dress tonight – I'm wearing it.

Knock knock.
Who's there?
Camilla.
Camilla who?
Camilla minute!

Knock knock.
Who's there?
Candace.
Candace who?
Candace be love?

Knock knock.
Who's there?
Carmen.
Carmen who?
Carmen like best is a Ferrari.

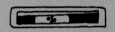

Knock knock.
Who's there?
Carol.
Carol who?
Carol go if you switch the ignition on.

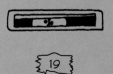

Knock knock.
Who's there?
Carrie.
Carrie who?
Carrie on with what you are doing.

Knock knock.
Who's there?
Cassie.
Cassie who?
Cassie you some time?

Knock knock.
Who's there?
Cecile.
Cecile who?
Cecile the envelope.

Knock knock.
Who's there?
Celeste.
Celeste who?
Celeste time I come calling.

Knock knock.
Who's there?
Cindy.
Cindy who?
Cindy parcel special delivery.

Knock knock.
Who's there?
Dana.
Dana who?
Dana you mind.

Knock knock.
Who's there?
Daryl.
Daryl who?
Daryl be the day.

Knock knock.
Who's there?
Dawn.
Dawn who?
Dawn do anything I wouldn't do.

Knock knock.
Who's there?
Della.
Della who?
Della tell ya that I love ya?

Knock knock.
Who's there?
Delphine.
Delphine who?
Delphine fine, thanks.

Knock knock.
Who's there?
Denise.
Denise who?
Denise are above de feet.

Knock knock.
Who's there?
Diana.
Diana who?
Diana thirst – a glass of water,
please.

Knock knock.
Who's there?
Dolly.
Dolly who?
Dolly't them in, they're dangerous.

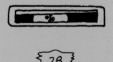

Knock knock.
Who's there?
Donna.
Donna who?
Donna you know? Isa Luigi.

Knock knock.
Who's there?
Dora.
Dora who?
Dora steel.

Knock knock.
Who's there?
Dorothy.
Dorothy who?
(sing) "Dorothynk I'm sexy?"

Knock knock.
Who's there?
Effie.
Effie who?
Effie'd known you were coming
he'd have stayed home.

Knock knock.
Who's there?
Elizabeth.
Elizabeth who?
Elizabeth of knowledge is a
dangerous thing.

Knock knock.
Who's there?
Ella.
Ella who?
Ella've good night!

Knock knock.
Who's there?
Ellen.
Ellen who?
Ellen high water.

Knock knock.
Who's there?
Miss Ellie.
Miss Ellie who?
Miss Ellie good shows lately?

Knock knock.
Who's there?
Elly.
Elly who?
Ellymentary, my dear Watson.

Knock knock.
Who's there?
Emma.
Emma who?
Emma new resident here – come round for tea.

Knock knock.
Who's there?
Enid.
Enid who?
Enid a glass of water.

Knock knock.
Who's there?
Erica.
Erica who?
Erica'd the last sweet.

Knock knock.
Who's there?
Erin.
Erin who?
Erin your lungs.

Knock knock.
Who's there?
Eunice.
Eunice who?
Eunice is like your nephew.

Knock knock.
Who's there?
Eva.
Eva who?
Eva had a smack in the mouth?

Knock knock.
Who's there?
Fanny.
Fanny who?
Fanny you not knowing who I am!

Knock knock.
Who's there?
Faye.
Faye who?
Fayeding away.

Knock knock.
Who's there?
Felicity.
Felicity who?
Felicity getting more polluted every
day.

Knock knock.
Who's there?
Fifi.
Fifi who?
Fifiling c-cold, p-please l-let m-me
in.

Knock knock.
Who's there?
Fiona.
Fiona who?
Fiona large house and a car.

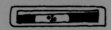

Knock knock.
Who's there?
Fleur.
Fleur who?
Fleuride toothpaste.

Knock knock.
Who's there?
Flo.
Flo who?
Flo your candles out.

Knock knock.
Who's there?
Flora.
Flora who?
Florat the top of the block.

Knock knock.
Who's there?
Flossie.
Flossie who?
Flossie your teeth every day.

Knock knock.
Who's there?
Francoise.
Francoise who?
Francoise once a great empire.

Knock knock.
Who's there?
Gail.
Gail who?
Gail of laughter.

Knock knock.
Who's there?
Germaine.
Germaine who?
Germaine you don't recognize me?

Knock knock.
Who's there?
Gertie.
Gertie who?
Gertiesy call!

Knock knock.
Who's there?
Gilda.
Gilda who?
Gilda the picture frame.

Knock knock.
Who's there?
Giselle.
Giselle who?
Gisellegant and very pretty.

Knock knock.
Who's there?
Gita.
Gita who?
Gita job!

Knock knock.
Who's there?
Gladys.
Gladys who?
Gladys letter isn't a bill.

Knock knock.
Who's there?
Grace.
Grace who?
Grace skies are over us.

Knock knock.
Who's there?
Greta.
Greta who?
Greta job.

Knock knock.
Who's there?
Guinevere.
Guinevere who?
Guinevere going to get together?

Knock knock.
Who's there?
Hannah.
Hannah who?
Hannah cloth out to dry.

Knock knock.
Who's there?
Harriet.
Harriet who?
Harriet up!

Knock knock.
Who's there?
Hazel.
Hazel who?
Hazel restrict your vision.

Knock knock.
Who's there?
Heather.
Heather who?
Heather pothtman come yet?

Knock knock.
Who's there?
Hedda.
Hedda who?
Hedda ball in goal.

Knock knock.
Who's there?
Heidi.
Heidi who?
Heidi Clare war on you.

Knock knock.
Who's there?
Holly.
Holly who?
Hollylujah!

Knock knock.
Who's there?
Hope.
Hope who?
Hope you'll have me.

Knock knock.
Who's there?
Ida.
Ida who?
Ida bought a different knocker if
I'd been you.

Knock knock.
Who's there?
Ida.
Ida who?
Ida know.

Knock knock.
Who's there?
Imogen.
Imogen who?
Imogenuine person.

Knock knock.
Who's there?
Ina.
Ina who?
Ina minute!

Knock knock.
Who's there?
Ina Claire.
Ina Claire who?
Ina Claire day you can see forever.

Knock knock.
Who's there?
Ina Minnie.
Ina Minnie who?
Ina Minnie miney mo.

Knock knock.
Who's there?
India.
India who?
India there's a bag belonging to
me.

Knock knock.
Who's there?
Ines.
Ines who?
Inespecial place I'll hide your
present.

Knock knock.
Who's there?
Ingrid.
Ingrid who?
Ingrid sorrow I have to leave you.

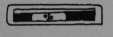

Knock knock.
Who's there?
Iona.
Iona who?
Iona house of my own, you know.

Knock knock.
Who's there?
Iris.
Iris who?
Iris you would open the door.

Knock knock.
Who's there?
Isabel.
Isabel who?
Isabel necessary on a bicycle?

Knock knock.
Who's there?
Isadore.
Isadore who?
Isadore on the right way round?

Knock knock.
Who's there?
Isla.
Isla who?
Isla be seeing you!

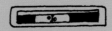

Knock knock.
Who's there?
Ivy.
Ivy who?
Ivyll cast a spell on you.

Knock knock.
Who's there?
Jackie.
Jackie who?
Jackie'n that job – it's killing you.

Knock knock.
Who's there?
Jacqueline.
Jacqueline who?
Jacqueline Hyde.

Knock knock.
Who's there?
Jade.
Jade who?
Jade a whole pie today.

Knock knock.
Who's there?
Jan.
Jan who?
Jan and bread.

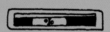

Knock knock.
Who's there?
Janet.
Janet who?
Janet a big fish?

Knock knock.
Who's there?
Jasmine.
Jasmine who?
Jasmine like to play in bands.

Knock knock.
Who's there?
Jean.
Jean who?
Jeanius – you just don't recognize it.

Knock knock.
Who's there?
Jeanette.
Jeanette who?
Jeanette has too many holes in it,
the fish will escape.

Knock knock.
Who's there?
Jenny.
Jenny who?
Jenny-d anything from the shops?

Knock knock.
Who's there?
Jessica.
Jessica who?
Jessica lot up last night?

Knock knock.
Who's there?
Joan.
Joan who?
Joan call us, we'll call you.

Knock knock.
Who's there?
Joanna.
Joanna who?
Joanna big kiss?

Knock knock.
Who's there?
Juanita.
Juanita who?
Juanita big meal?

Knock knock.
Who's there?
Judy.
Judy who?
Judy liver newspapers still?

Knock knock.
Who's there?
Julie.
Julie who?
Julie'n on this door a lot?

Knock knock.
Who's there?
Juliet.
Juliet who?
Juliet him get away with that?

Knock knock.
Who's there?
June.
June who?
June know how to open a door?

Knock knock.
Who's there?
Juno.
Juno who?
Juno how to get out of here?

Knock knock.
Who's there?
Justine.
Justine who?
Justine case.

Knock knock.
Who's there?
Katherine.
Katherine who?
Katherine together for a social evening.

Knock knock.
Who's there?
Kathy.
Kathy who?
Kathy you again?

Knock knock.
Who's there?
Kiki.
Kiki who?
Kiki's stuck in the lock – let me in.

Knock knock.
Who's there?
Kim.
Kim who?
Kim too late.

Knock knock.
Who's there?
Kristin.
Kristin who?
Kristining robe.

Knock knock.
Who's there?
Lacey.
Lacey who?
Lacey crazy days.

Knock knock.
Who's there?
Lana.
Lana who?
Lana the free.

Knock knock.
Who's there?
Lee.
Lee who?
Lee've it to me.

Knock knock.
Who's there?
Leonie.
Leonie who.
Leonie one I love.

Knock knock.
Who's there?
Leslie.
Leslie who?
Leslie town now before they catch us.

Knock knock.
Who's there?
Lily.
Lily who?
Lily livered varmint!

Knock knock.
Who's there?
Liz.
Liz who?
Liz see what you look like.

Knock knock.
Who's there?
Lotte.
Lotte who?
Lotte sense.

Knock knock.
Who's there?
Louise.
Louise who?
Louise coming to tea today.

Knock knock.
Who's there?
Lucetta.
Lucetta who?
Lucetta a difficult problem.

Knock knock.
Who's there?
Lucille.
Lucille who?
Lucille-ing is dangerous to live
under.

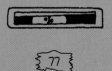

Knock knock.
Who's there?
Lucinda.
Lucinda who?
(sing) "Lucinda sky with
diamonds . . ."

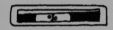

Knock knock.
Who's there?
Lucy.
Lucy who?
Lucylastic can let you down.

Knock knock.
Who's there?
Mae.
Mae who?
(sing) "Mae be it's because I'm a Londoner."

Knock knock.
Who's there?
Margo.
Margo who?
Margo, you're not needed now.

Knock knock.
Who's there?
Maria.
Maria who?
Marial name is Mary.

Knock knock.
Who's there?
Marian.
Marian who?
Mariand her little lamb.

Knock knock.
Who's there?
Marie.
Marie who?
Marie for love.

Knock knock.
Who's there?
Marietta.
Marietta who?
Marietta whole loaf!

Knock knock.
Who's there?
Marilyn.
Marilyn who?
Marilyn, she'll make you a good wife.

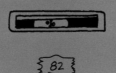

Knock knock.
Who's there?
Marion.
Marion who?
Marion idiot and repent at leisure.

Knock knock.
Who's there?
Martha.
Martha who?
Martha boys next door are hurting me!

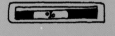

Knock knock.
Who's there?
Mary.
Mary who?
That's what I keep wondering.

Knock knock.
Who's there?
Maude.
Maude who?
Mauden my job's worth.

Knock knock.
Who's there?
Mavis.
Mavis who?
Mavis be the best day of your life.

Knock knock.
Who's there?
Maxine.
Maxine who?
Maxine a lot of things.

Knock knock.
Who's there?
May.
May who?
Maybe it's a friend at the door.

Knock knock.
Who's there?
Maya.
Maya who?
Maya turn.

Knock knock.
Who's there?
Meg.
Meg who?
Meg a fuss.

Knock knock.
Who's there?
Megan.
Megan who?
Megan a loud noise.

Knock knock.
Who's there?
Michelle.
Michelle who?
Michelle has sounds of the sea
in it.

Knock knock.
Who's there?
Mimi.
Mimi who?
Mimi b-bicycle's b-broken.

Knock knock.
Who's there?
Minnie.
Minnie who?
Minnie people want to come in.

Knock knock.
Who's there?
Miranda.
Miranda who?
Miranda friend want to come in.

Knock knock.
Who's there.
Nadia.
Nadia who?
Nadia head if you want to come in.

Knock knock.
Who's there?
Nancy.
Nancy who?
Nancy a piece of cake?

Knock knock.
Who's there?
Nicky.
Nicky who?
Nicky nacks.

Knock knock.
Who's there?
Nola.
Nola who?
Nolaner driver may drive a car
alone.

Knock knock.
Who's there?
Norma.
Norma who?
Normally the butler opens the door.

Knock knock.
Who's there?
Olga.
Olga who?
Olga home now.

Knock knock.
Who's there?
Olive.
Olive who?
Olive in this house – what are you
doing there?

Knock knock.
Who's there?
Olivia.
Olivia who?
Olivia'l is great for cooking.

Knock knock.
Who's there?
Onya.
Onya who?
Onya marks, get set, go.

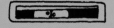

Knock knock.
Who's there?
Pam.
Pam who?
Pamper yourself.

Knock knock.
Who's there?
Pammy.
Pammy who?
Pammy something nice when you
are at the shops!

Knock knock.
Who's there?
Patty.
Patty who?
Patty-cake.

Knock knock.
Who's there?
Peg.
Peg who?
Peg your pardon, I've got the wrong door.

Knock knock.
Who's there?
Penny.
Penny who?
Penny for your thoughts.

Knock knock.
Who's there?
Petal.
Petal who?
Petal fast, we're nearly there.

Knock knock.
Who's there?
Phoebe.
Phoebe who?
Phoebe way above my price.

Knock knock.
Who's there?
Phyllis.
Phyllis who?
Phyllis up.

Knock knock.
Who's there?
Polly.
Polly who?
Polly the other one, it's got bells on.

Knock knock.
Who's there?
Poppy.
Poppy who?
Poppy'n any time you like.

Knock knock.
Who's there?
Portia.
Portia who?
Portia the door – it's stuck.

Knock knock.
Who's there?
Rena.
Rena who?
Renamok in the shopping mall.

Knock knock.
Who's there?
Renata.
Renata who?
Renata sugar. Can I borrow some?

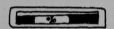

Knock knock.
Who's there?
Rhona.
Rhona who?
Rhonaround town.

Knock knock.
Who's there?
Rhonda.
Rhonda who?
Rhonda why?

Knock knock.
Who's there?
Rita.
Rita who?
Rita novel.

Knock knock.
Who's there?
Rose.
Rose who?
Rose early one morning.

Knock knock.
Who's there?
Rosina.
Rosina who?
Rosina vase.

Knock knock.
Who's there?
Ruth.
Ruth who?
Ruthless people.

Knock knock.
Who's there?
Saffron.
Saffron who?
Saffron a chair and it collapsed.

Knock knock.
Who's there?
Sally.
Sally who?
Sallyeverything you've got.

Knock knock.
Who's there?
Samantha.
Samantha who?
Samantha baby have gone for a
walk.

Knock knock.
Who's there?
Sandra.
Sandra who?
Sandrabout your toes on the
beach.

Knock knock.
Who's there?
Sandy.
Sandy who?
Sandy shore.

Knock knock.
Who's there?
Sarah.
Sarah who?
Sarah doctor in the house?

Knock knock.
Who's there?
Serena.
Serena who?
Serena round the corner.

Knock knock.
Who's there?
Sharon.
Sharon who?
Sharon share alike – would you
like some of my chocolate?

Knock knock.
Who's there?
Shelby.
Shelby who?
(sing) "Shelby coming round the mountain when she comes."

Knock knock.
Who's there?
Sherry.
Sherry who?
Sherry trifle!

Knock knock.
Who's there?
Shirley.
Shirley who?
Shirley you know who I am!

Knock knock.
Who's there?
Sonia.
Sonia who?
Sonia shoe – it's stinking the
house out.

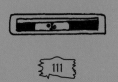

Knock knock.
Who's there?
Stacey.
Stacey who?
Stacey what happens next.

Knock knock.
Who's there?
Stella.
Stella who?
Stella lot from the rich people.

Knock knock.
Who's there?
Stephanie.
Stephanie who?
Stephanie gas – we need to go faster!

Knock knock.
Who's there?
Sue.
Sue who?
Sue'n you will know.

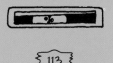

Knock knock.
Who's there?
Sybil.
Sybil who?
Sybiling rivalry.

Knock knock.
Who's there?
Tamsin.
Tamsin who?
Tamsin time again I come to the
wrong house.

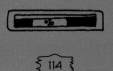

Knock knock.
Who's there?
Tania.
Tania who?
Tania self round, you'll see.

Knock knock.
Who's there?
Tara.
Tara who?
Tararaboomdeay.

Knock knock.
Who's there?
Tiffany.
Tiffany who?
Tiffany rubbish out of the bag
before you use it.

Knock knock.
Who's there?
Tilly.
Tilly who?
Tilly cows come home.

Knock knock.
Who's there?
Tina.
Tina who?
Tina tomatoes.

Knock knock.
Who's there?
Tori.
Tori who?
Tori I upset you.

Knock knock.
Who's there?
Tracy.
Tracy who?
Tracy the shape in pencil.

Knock knock.
Who's there?
Tricia.
Tricia who?
Bless you – what a bad cold!

Knock knock.
Who's there?
Trudy.
Trudy who?
Trudy your word.

Knock knock.
Who's there?
Una.
Una who?
Yes, Una who.

Knock knock.
Who's there?
Utica.
Utica who?
(sing) "Utica high road and I'll
take the low road."

Knock knock.
Who's there?
Vanda.
Vanda who?
Vanda you vant me to come round?

Knock knock.
Who's there?
Vanessa.
Vanessa who?
Vanessa time I'll ring the bell.

Knock knock.
Who's there?
Viola.
Viola who?
Viola sudden you don't know
who I am?

Knock knock.
Who's there?
Violet.
Violet who?
Violet the cat out of the bag.

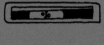

Knock knock.
Who's there?
Wendy.
Wendy who?
Wendy come to take you away
I won't stop them!

Knock knock.
Who's there?
Willa.
Willa who?
Willa present make you happy?

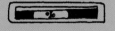

Knock knock.
Who's there?
Winnie.
Winnie who?
Winnie is better than losing.

Knock knock.
Who's there?
Xena.
Xena who?
Xena minute!

Knock knock.
Who's there?
Yvette.
Yvette who?
Yvette helps lots of animals.

Knock knock.
Who's there?
Yvonne.
Yvonne who?
Yvonne to know vat you are doing.

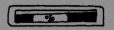

Knock knock.
Who's there?
Zoe.
Zoe who?
Zoe said that, did he? Don't
believe him.

Boys' Names

Knock knock.
Who's there?
Aaron.
Aaron who?
Aaron the chest means strength in arms.

Knock knock.
Who's there?
Abel.
Abel who?
Abel to go to work.

Knock knock.
Who's there?
Adair.
Adair who?
Adair you to open this door.

Knock knock.
Who's there?
Adam.
Adam who?
Adam nuisance come to borrow
some sugar.

Knock knock.
Who's there?
Al.
Al who?
Al be seeing you!

Knock knock.
Who's there?
Alan.
Alan who?
Alan a good cause.

Knock knock.
Who's there?
Albert.
Albert who?
Albert you'll never guess.

Knock knock.
Who's there?
Aldo.
Aldo who?
Aldo the washing up tonight.

Knock knock.
Who's there?
Alec.
Alec who?
Alec your sister but I don't like you.

Knock knock.
Who's there?
Alex.
Alex who?
Alex plain later if you let me in.

Knock knock.
Who's there?
Alexander.
Alexander who?
Alexander friend want to come
over.

Knock knock.
Who's there?
Alf.
Alf who?
Alf way home.

Knock knock.
Who's there?
Alfie.
Alfie who?
Alfie terrible if you leave.

Knock knock.
Who's there?
Alistair.
Alistair who?
Alistairs in this house are broken.

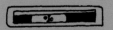

Knock knock.
Who's there?
Alvin.
Alvin who?
Alvin zis competition – just vait and see!

Knock knock.
Who's there?
Amos.
Amos who?
Amos be mad! This isn't my house.

Knock knock.
Who's there?
Andrew.
Andrew who?
Andrew a picture on the wall.

Knock knock.
Who's there?
Andy.
Andy who?
Andy man.

Knock knock.
Who's there?
Arnie.
Arnie who?
Arnie going to let me in?

Knock knock.
Who's there?
Arnold.
Arnold who?
Arnold man.

Knock knock.
Who's there?
Asa.
Asa who?
Asa glass of orange out of the
question?

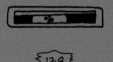

Knock knock.
Who's there?
Barry.
Barry who?
Barry the dead.

Knock knock.
Who's there?
Ben.
Ben who?
Ben down and tie your shoelaces.

Knock knock.
Who's there?
Benjamin.
Benjamin who.
Benjamin the blues.

Knock knock.
Who's there?
Bernie.
Bernie who?
Bernie bridges.

Knock knock.
Who's there?
Bert.
Bert who?
Bert the cakes.

Knock knock.
Who's there?
Bill.
Bill who?
Bill of rights.

Knock knock.
Who's there?
Bjorn.
Bjorn who?
Bjorn free.

Knock knock.
Who's there?
Bobby.
Bobby who?
Bobbyn up and down like this.

Knock knock.
Who's there?
Brian.
Brian who?
Brian drain!

Knock knock.
Who's there?
Brad.
Brad who?
Brad to meet ya!

Knock knock.
Who's there?
Brendan.
Brendan who?
Brendan ear to what I have to say.

Knock knock.
Who's there?
Bruno.
Bruno who?
Bruno more tea for me.

Knock knock.
Who's there?
Buster.
Buster who?
Buster the town, please.

Knock knock.
Who's there?
Caesar.
Caesar who?
Caesar jolly good fellow.

Knock knock.
Who's there?
Cain.
Cain who?
Cain tell you.

Knock knock.
Who's there?
Callum.
Callum who?
Callum all back.

Knock knock.
Who's there?
Carl.
Carl who?
Carl you see?

Knock knock.
Who's there?
Charles.
Charles who?
Charles your luck on the roulette wheel.

Knock knock.
Who's there?
Chester.
Chester who?
Chester minute! Don't you know
who I am?

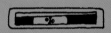

Knock knock.
Who's there?
Chris.
Chris who?
Chrismas stocking.

Knock knock.
Who's there?
Chuck.
Chuck who?
Chuck in a sandwich for lunch!

Knock knock.
Who's there?
Cliff.
Cliff who?
Cliffhanger.

Knock knock.
Who's there?
Cohen.
Cohen who?
Cohen your way.

Knock knock.
Who's there?
Colin.
Colin who?
Colin all cars . . . Colin all cars . . .

Knock knock.
Who's there?
Cosmo.
Cosmo who?
Cosmo trouble than you're worth.

Knock knock.
Who's there?
Costas.
Costas who?
Costas a fortune to get here.

Knock knock.
Who's there?
Craig.
Craig who?
Craig in the wall.

Knock knock.
Who's there?
Crispin.
Crispin who?
Crispin crunchy is how I like my cereal.

Knock knock.
Who's there?
Cyril.
Cyril who?
Cyril animals at the zoo.

Knock knock.
Who's there?
Dale.
Dale who?
Dale come if you call dem.

Knock knock.
Who's there?
Danny.
Danny who?
Dannybody home?

Knock knock.
Who's there?
Darren.
Darren who?
Darren the garden, hiding.

Knock knock.
Who's there?
Dave.
Dave who?
Dave of glory.

Knock knock.
Who's there?
Derek.
Derek who?
Derek get richer and the poor get poorer.

Knock knock.
Who's there?
Desi.
Desi who?
Desi take sugar?

Knock knock.
Who's there?
Devlin.
Devlin who?
Devlin a red dress.

Knock knock.
Who's there?
Dewey.
Dewey who?
Dewey stay or do we go now?

Knock knock.
Who's there?
Diego.
Diego who?
Diego before de "B".

Knock knock.
Who's there?
Don.
Don who?
Don take me for granted.

Knock knock.
Who's there?
Douglas.
Douglas who?
Douglas is broken.

Knock knock.
Who's there?
Duane.
Duane who?
Duane gonna get away with dis!

Knock knock.
Who's there?
Duncan.
Duncan who?
Duncan biscuit in your tea.

Knock knock.
Who's there?
Dwight.
Dwight who?
Dwight house is where the
president lives.

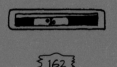

Knock knock.
Who's there?
Eamon.
Eamon who?
Eamon a good mood – have my
piece of cake.

Knock knock.
Who's there?
Earl.
Earl who?
Earl tell you if you open the door.

Knock knock.
Who's there?
Eddie.
Eddie who?
Eddie-body you like.

Knock knock.
Who's there?
Edward.
Edward who?
Edward like to play now, please.

Knock knock.
Who's there?
Edwin.
Edwin who?
Edwin a cup if I could run faster.

Knock knock.
Who's there?
Egbert.
Egbert who?
Egbert no bacon.

Knock knock.
Who's there?
Eli.
Eli who?
Eli, eli, oh!

Knock knock.
Who's there?
Ellis.
Ellis who?
Ellis damnation.

Knock knock.
Who's there?
Emil.
Emil who?
Emil would be nice if you've got
some food.

Knock knock.
Who's there?
Emmett.
Emmett who?
Emmett the front door, not the
back.

Knock knock.
Who's there?
Ethan.
Ethan who?
Ethan all my dinner.

Knock knock.
Who's there?
Eugene.
Eugene who?
Eugene, me Tarzan.

Knock knock.
Who's there?
Evan.
Evan who?
Evan only knows!

Knock knock.
Who's there?
Ewan.
Ewan who?
Ewan me should get together.

Knock knock.
Who's there?
Ezra.
Ezra who?
Ezra room to rent?

Knock knock.
Who's there?
Felix.
Felix who?
Felixtremely cold.

Knock knock.
Who's there?
Fido.
Fido who?
Fido known you were coming I'd
have baked a cake.

Knock knock.
Who's there?
Fletcher.
Fletcher who?
Fletcher stick, there's a good boy.

Knock knock.
Who's there?
Foster.
Foster who?
Foster than a speeding bullet.

Knock knock.
Who's there?
Francis.
Francis who?
Francis where the French live.

Knock knock.
Who's there?
Frank.
Frank who?
Frank you very much.

Knock knock.
Who's there?
Franz.
Franz who?
Franz, Romans, countrymen, lend
me your ears.

Knock knock.
Who's there?
Fred.
Fred who?
Fred this needle – I'm cross-eyed.

Knock knock.
Who's there?
Freddie.
Freddie who?
Freddie won't come out to play today.

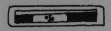

Knock knock.
Who's there?
Gary.
Gary who?
Gary on smiling.

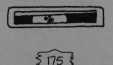

Knock knock.
Who's there?
Geoff.
Geoff who?
Geoff feel like going out tonight?

Knock knock.
Who's there?
Giuseppe.
Giuseppe who?
Giuseppe credit cards?

CREATING THE
FUTURE NOW

> The future is sending back good wishes
> and waiting with open arms.
>
> —KOBI YAMADA

You'll find lots of good advice in these pages, and some of it you may have even heard before: Stay ahead of the curve. Anticipate the next step. Always have your next idea waiting in the wings. Stay light on your feet, not entrenched. Champion change and innovation. And always be willing to give up the good to go for the great.

In the past these little axioms were fun to read, but today they are crucial keys to survival. We are living and working in a time of unprecedented change. Overnight, changes in technology can fundamentally imperil not only what a company makes but how the product is made and delivered. The rate of change will get faster, not slower. That spells great opportunity or potential disaster, depending on how you and your company choose to handle it.

"A company must be willing to change faster than the world around it," warns a report from General Electric. "You either do what's necessary to remain the best at what you do, or you don't get to do it for very long."

The truth is, most companies die prematurely, and the number one killer is resistance to change, otherwise known as "hardening of the attitudes."

Be a company that thrives. Choose to be an agent of change rather than a victim of change. Relax, have fun, and welcome what comes next with open arms.

WHAT'S
NEXT

TO STAY AHEAD, YOU MUST HAVE YOUR NEXT IDEA WAITING IN THE WINGS.

—ROSABETH MOSS KANTER

Business is an instinctive exercise in foresight.

—HENRY LUCE

Always be on the lookout for the big idea
that can change your life.

—NORMAN VINCENT PEALE

See things as you would have them be,
instead of as they are.

—ROBERT COLLIER

WHAT'S
NEXT

We are called upon to become creators, to make the world new and in that sense to bring something into being which was not there before.
—JOHN ELOF BOODIN

You alone, of all the animals, have the ability to reconstruct what has gone before, to learn from it, and to envision the future shape of things to come. What a faculty! Why waste it on meaningless pursuits?
—DON WARD

I am in the world to change the world.
—MURIEL RUKEYSER

The future belongs to those who see
possibilities before they become obvious.
—JOHN SCULLEY

Look at things not as they are, but as they
can be. Visualization adds value to everything.
A big thinker always visualizes what can be done
in the future. You aren't stuck with the present.
—DAVID SCHWARTZ

Just think of something that would be
"wonderful" if it were only "possible."
Then set out to make it possible.
—ARMAND HAMMER

WHAT'S
NEXT

**YOU SHALL
SEE WONDERS.**

–WILLIAM SHAKESPEARE

We live in a wonderful world that is full of beauty, charm and adventure. There is no end to the adventures that we can have if only we seek them with our eyes open.

—JAWAHARAL NEHRU

There aren't just seven wonders of the world. There are more like seven million.

—KOBI YAMADA

The most beautiful thing we can experience is the mysterious. It is the source of all true art and science. He who can no longer pause to wonder and stand rapt in awe is as good as dead: his eyes are closed.

—ALBERT EINSTEIN

WHAT'S
NEXT

Wisdom begins in wonder.

—SOCRATES

I would rather have a mind opened
by wonder than closed by belief.

—GERRY SPENCE

The larger the island of knowledge,
the greater the shoreline of wonder.

—RALPH STOCKMAN

Never lose your sense of wonder.
—JOE BATTEN

All change is a miracle to contemplate;
but it is a miracle which is taking place
every instant.
—HENRY DAVID THOREAU

This is the gift—to have the wonderful capacity to
appreciate again and again, freshly and naively,
the basic goods of life, with awe, pleasure,
wonder, and even ecstasy.
—ABRAHAM MASLOW

WHAT'S
NEXT

TO FIND AN OPEN ROAD, HAVE AN OPEN MIND.

–JOHN TOWNE

I can't understand why people are frightened of new ideas. I'm frightened of the old ones.
—JOHN CAGE

For 1,500 years, the Earth was the center of the Solar System simply because Claudius Ptolemy said so.
—DAN ZADRA

The difficulty lies not so much in developing new ideas as in escaping from the old ones.
—JOHN MAYNARD KEYNES

WHAT'S
NEXT

We aren't forced to follow the old ideas.
—J. GEORGE BENDORZ

Creative thinking may simply mean the realization that there's no particular virtue in doing things the way we have always done them.
—RUDOLPH FLESCH

The innovator is not an opponent of the old, he is a proponent of the new.
—LYLE E. SHALLER

The more original a discovery, the more
obvious it seems afterward.

—ARTHUR KOESTLER

At first people refuse to believe that a strange
new thing can be done, then they begin to hope
it can be done, then they see it can be done.
Then it is done and all the world wonders why
it was not done centuries ago.

—FRANCES H. BURNETT

WHAT'S
NEXT

Few of us take the pains to study the origin of our cherished convictions.

—J. H. ROBINSON

The conventional view serves to protect us from the painful job of thinking.

—JOHN KENNETH GALBRAITH

Read, every day, something no one else is reading. Think, every day, something no one else is thinking. It is bad for the mind to be always part of unanimity.

—CHRISTOPHER MORLEY

Whenever you find yourself on the side of the majority, it is time to pause and reflect.

—MARK TWAIN

All progress has resulted from people who took unpopular positions.

—ADLAI STEVENSON

Somebody is always doing what somebody else said couldn't be done.

—UNKNOWN

WHAT'S
NEXT

THE MOST POWERFUL AGENT OF CHANGE IS A CHANGE OF HEART.

—GIL ATKINSON

It often takes more courage to change one's opinion than to stick to it.
—GEORG CHRISTOPH LICHTENBERG

All breakthroughs begin with a change in beliefs.
—MICHAEL NOLAN

If you don't change your beliefs, your life will be like this forever. Is that good news?
—ROBERT ANTHONY

WHAT'S NEXT

Living involves tearing up one rough draft after another.

—UNKNOWN

The first rule of holes: If you find yourself in one, stop digging.

—JACK DANE

Surely this must be an ancient proverb:
If the situation is killing you or your company, get the hell out.

—HUGH PRATHER

When you're stuck in a spiral, to change all aspects of the spin you need only to change one thing.

—CHRISTINA BALDWIN

Not knowing it all is no excuse not to start.

—JUDY COLUMBUS

The important thing is this: to be willing at any moment to sacrifice what we are for what we could become.

—CHARLES DU BOS

WHAT'S
NEXT

IF YOUR HORSE DIES, GET OFF.

—OLD BUSINESS AXIOM

As important as "hanging on" is knowing when to let go.

—SHERRI DEWITT

Businessmen go down with their businesses because they like the old way so well they cannot bring themselves to change.

—HENRY FORD

Every organization has to prepare for the abandonment of everything it does.

—PETER DRUCKER

WHAT'S NEXT

Constants aren't.

—JOHN PEERS

Since life is growth and motion, a fixed point
of view kills anybody who has one.

—BROOKS ATKINSON

If you are standing still, you're falling
way behind.

—UNKNOWN

It is not only for what we do that we are held responsible, but also for what we do not do.
—MOLIÈRE

The tendency to follow the path of least resistance guarantees failure in life.
—BRIAN TRACY

Changes are not only possible and predictable, but to deny them is to be an accomplice to one's own necessary vegetation.
—GAIL SHEEHY

WHAT'S
NEXT

THE FIRST RULE OF SURVIVAL IS CLEAR: NOTHING IS MORE DANGEROUS THAN YESTERDAY'S SUCCESS.

—ALVIN TOFFLER

Whatever made you successful in the past won't in the future.

—LEW PLATT, HEWLETT PACKARD

Not all organizations adapt equally well to the environment within which they grow. Many, like the dinosaur, remain unchanged in a changing world.

—CHARLES HANDY

It is a fact of history that those who seek to withdraw from its great experiments usually end up being overwhelmed by them.

—BARBARA WARD

WHAT'S
NEXT

Conformity is the jailer of freedom and the enemy of growth.

—JOHN F. KENNEDY

Consistency is the last refuge of the unimaginative.

—OSCAR WILDE

In spite of warnings, nothing much happens until the status quo becomes more painful than change.

—LAURENCE J. PETER

We cannot become what we need to be by remaining what we are.

—MAX DE PREE

The future is made in the present.

—KELLY ANDREWS

Someday. Tomorrow. Eventually.
Three of the worst times to start planning your business continuance.

—COMPUTER ASSOCIATES ADVERSTISEMENT

WHAT'S
NEXT

PEOPLE WHO ARE RESTING ON THEIR LAURELS ARE WEARING THEM ON THE WRONG END.

—MALCOLM KUSHNER

It will be a great thing for the human soul
when it finally stops worshipping backwards.
—CHARLOTTE P. GILMAN

You can spend your life looking over
your shoulder, or you can spend your life
looking ahead.
—PLEASANT ROWLAND

The past is finished. There is nothing to be
gained by going over it. Whatever it gave us
in the experiences it brought us was something
we had to know—but, let's move on.
—REBECCA BEARD

WHAT'S
NEXT

The hardest person to awaken is the one already awake.

—TAGALOG SAYING

It's easy to come up with new ideas;
the hard part is letting go of what worked for
you two years ago, but will soon be out-of-date.

—ROGER VON OECH

Faced with the choice between changing one's
mind or proving that there is no need to do so,
almost everybody gets busy on the proof.

—JOHN KENNETH GALBRAITH

A closed mind is like a closed book:
just a block of wood.

—CHINESE PROVERB

You may send a message around the world
in one seventh of a second, yet it may take years
to force a simple idea through a quarter inch
of a human skull.

—CHARLES KETTERING

Your brain is not a museum for the past, or a
lumber room for the present; it is a laboratory
for the future.

—JOHN FREDERICK CHARLES FULLER

WHAT'S
NEXT

Dissatisfaction is the basis of progress.
When we become satisfied, we become obsolete.

—J. WILLIARD MARRIOTT, JR.

Intelligent discontent is the mainspring of
civilization. Progress is born of agitation.
It is agitation or stagnation.

—EUGENE V. DEBS

I wish I were with some of the wild people
that run in the woods, and know nothing about
accomplishments!

—JOANNA BAILLIE

It's more fun to build a future—not just polish the past.
—FRANK VIZZARE

"The good old days."
The only good days are ahead.
—ALICE CHILDRESS

If your mind isn't open, please keep your mouth shut.
—SUE GRAFTON

WHAT'S
NEXT

CHANGE IS GOOD—YOU GO FIRST!

—GRAFFITI

There are two ways to face the future.
One way is with apprehension; the other is
with anticipation.

—JIM ROHN

It takes a lot of courage to release the familiar
and seemingly secure, to embrace the new.
But there is no real security in what is no longer
meaningful. There is more security in the
adventurous and exciting; for in movement
and change there is life.

—ALAN COHEN

I find the great thing in this world is not
so much where we stand, as in what direction
we are moving.

—OLIVER WENDELL HOLMES

In actual life every great enterprise begins
with and takes its first forward step in faith.

—FRIEDRICH VON SCHLEGEL

Yes, creation is moving toward us; life is moving
toward us all the time. We back away, but it
keeps pushing toward us. Why not step forward
and greet it.

—JOAN HALIFAX

I have enjoyed life a lot more by saying yes
than by saying no.
—RICHARD BRANSON

We don't have to be afraid of change.
We don't have to worry about what's been taken
away. Just look to see what's been added.
—JACKIE GREER

I will not die an unlived life. I will not live in fear
of falling or catching fire. I choose to inhabit my
days, to allow my living to open me, to make me
less afraid, more accessible, to loosen my heart
until it becomes a wing, a torch, a promise.
—DAWNA MARKOVA

WHAT'S
NEXT

SOME PEOPLE
SHOULD HAVE
THEIR TOMBSTONE
INSCRIBED:
"DIED AT 40.
BURIED AT 80."

—BOB MOAWAD

Tradition does not mean that the living are dead;
it means that the dead are living.
—HAROLD MACMILLAN

Let tradition be your guide, but not your jailer.
—W. SOMERSET MAUGHAM

The hardest thing to believe when you're young
is that people will fight to stay in a rut, but not to
get out of it.
—ELLEN GLASGOW

WHAT'S
NEXT

We live only part of the life we are given.
—MICHAEL MURPHY

The life you have led doesn't need to be
the only life you have.
—ANNA QUINDLEN

If you have accomplished all that you
have planned for yourself, you have not
planned enough.
—EDWARD EVERETT HALE

It isn't where we came from;
it's where we're going that counts.
—ELLA FITZGERALD

Don't say you don't have enough time.
You have exactly the same number of hours
per day that were given to Helen Keller, Pasteur,
Michelangelo, Mother Teresa, Leonardo da Vinci,
Thomas Jefferson and Albert Einstein.
—H. JACKSON BROWN, JR.

How will you know if your mission on earth
is finished? If you're alive, it isn't.
—RICHARD BACH

WHAT'S
NEXT

LIFE IS BETWEEN THE TRAPEZE BARS.

—HELEN KELLER

Here's my one word secret to success:
Anticipation.
—DONALD REGAN

Opportunity waits between things ended
and things begun.
—KOBI YAMADA

Practice anticipatory thinking. What is likely
to happen and what will you do then?
—BRIAN TRACY

WHAT'S
NEXT

Between the wish and the thing life lies waiting.
—UNKNOWN

Anticipate opportunities and problems.
An ounce of prevention is worth a pound of cure.
That's a return of sixteen to one!
—LARRY MALINOWSKI, PH.D.

I anticipate criticism, competition and difficulties,
and that's the simple secret of avoiding problems
and failure.
—FRANK VIZZARE

Today I live in the quiet, joyous expectation
of good.
—ERNEST HOLMES

Around the corner of the street who can say
what waits for us?
—JAMES WHITCOMB RILEY

Live your life as though there is great joy to be
experienced around each curve in the road,
an abundance of goodness in each person you
come in contact with and the knowledge that
you have enough inner wisdom to answer the
mysteries that challenge you.
—MELADEE McCARTY

WHAT'S
NEXT

THE POINT OF LIVING IS TO BELIEVE THE BEST IS YET TO COME.

—PETER USTINOV

The future was plump with promise.

—MAYA ANGELOU

We are haunted by an ideal life, and it is because we have within us the beginning and the possibility of it.

—PHILLIPS BROOKS

We are not going to succeed in everything we attempt in life. That's a guarantee. In fact, the more we do in life, the more chance there is not to succeed in some things. But what a rich life we are having! Win or lose, we just keep winning.

—SUSAN JEFFERS

WHAT'S
NEXT

I always loved change, something new.
Change is a challenge, an excitement.

—DAWN SIBLEY

I believe that to win in life, you've got to become
a dreamer again. You've got to become excited
and "turned on" about your life and your future.

—ART WILLIAMS

There is one thing that gives radiance to
everything. It is the idea of something just
around the corner.

—G.K. CHESTERTON

The passion to make and make again.
—ADRIENNE RICH

Over the years I have discovered that ideas come through an intense desire for them; continually desiring, the mind becomes a watchtower on the lookout for incidents that may excite the imagination.
—CHARLIE CHAPLIN

Nobody is bored when he is trying to make something that is beautiful or to discover something that is true.
—WILLIAM RALPH INGE

WHAT'S
NEXT

BEWARE WHEN THE GREAT GOD LETS LOOSE A THINKER ON THIS PLANET.

—RALPH WALDO EMERSON

Big results require big ambitions.
—JAMES CHAMPY

It is the business of the future to be dangerous.
—ALFRED NORTH WHITEHEAD

Boldness, more boldness, and always boldness!
—GEORGE JACQUES DANTON

WHAT'S
NEXT

Be a Columbus to whole new continents
and worlds within you, opening new channels,
not of trade, but of thought.

—HENRY DAVID THOREAU

Once you realize that there are no geniuses
out there, you can think, "I can do that."
One reason I've succeeded is that I have
that naive sense of entitlement.

—DONNY DEUTSCH

Create the future rather than fear it.

—JOHN A. WARDEN

Let us see whether we also, in our day and generation, may not perform something worthy to be remembered.
—DANIEL WEBSTER

What will you do today that will matter tomorrow?
—RALPH MARSTON

Every project we take on starts with a question: How can we do what's never been done before?
—POLLY BABARRE

WHAT'S
NEXT

NO CRIME IS SO GREAT AS DARING TO EXCEL.

—WINSTON CHURCHILL

In the republic of mediocrity, genius is dangerous.
—ROBERT G. INGERSOLL

Whenever you take a step forward, you are bound to disturb something.
—INDIRA GANDHI

The future is made in the present. People either embrace new ideas or they crush them.
—DAVID LAMM

WHAT'S
NEXT

Dare to risk public criticism.

—MARY KAY ASH

The world in general doesn't know what to make of originality; it is startled out of its comfortable habits of thought, and its first reaction is one of anger.

—W. SOMERSET MAUGHM

For every action there is an equal and opposite criticism.

—STEVEN WRIGHT

If you don't make waves, you're not under way.
—LEONARD P. GOLLOBIN

If we are going to have ideas ahead of the times, we will have to get used to living with the fact that most people are going to believe we are in the wrong.
—BRUCE LLOYD

You always get negative reactions. If you worry about that, you would never do anything.
—TOM MONAGHAN

WHAT'S
NEXT

You can't please everybody if you are going to make a difference in this world.

—MELVIN CHAPMAN

The reward for conformity is everyone likes you but yourself.

—RITA MAE BROWN

What could you achieve in life if you decided to become totally and blissfully impervious to hostile criticism and to rejection?

—GARY S. GOODMAN

It never pays to deal with the flyweights of the world. They take far too much pleasure in thwarting you at every turn.

—SUE GRAFTON

Isn't it better to be making the news rather than taking it; to be an actor rather than a critic?

—WINSTON CHURCHILL

No pessimist ever discovered the secrets of the stars, or sailed to an uncharted land, or opened a new heaven to the human spirit.

—HELEN KELLER

WHAT'S
NEXT

THEY TRASHED THE RULES AND FOUND NEW WAYS TO WIN.

—MARK ROMAN

Where minds are open, there will always be
a frontier.

—ANONYMOUS

The world is before you, and you need not take
it or leave it as it was when you came in.

—JAMES BALDWIN

Things are only impossible until they're not.

—JEAN-LUC PICARD

WHAT'S
NEXT

Rules and models destroy genius and art.
—WILLIAM HAZLITT

**If you have always done it that way,
it is probably wrong.**
—CHARLES KETTERING

**Yesterday's answer has nothing to do with
today's problem.**
—BILL GATES

We can't solve problems by using the same
kind of thinking we used when we created them.

—ALBERT EINSTEIN

Discoveries are often made by not following
instructions, by going off the main road,
by trying the untried.

—FRANK TYGER

Don't be confined by reality or precedent.
Think about what could be accomplished if
there were no boundaries.

—JAMES FANTUS

WHAT'S
NEXT

Loyalty to a petrified opinion never yet broke
a chain or freed a human soul.
—MARK TWAIN

Not only have I broken all the rules
I learned about—I have broken rules I didn't
even know existed.
—MARTIN SCORSESE

There was never a great character who
did not sometimes smash the routine regulations
and make new ones for himself.
—ANDREW CARNEGIE

Without deviation from the norm, progress is not possible.
—C. D. JACKSON

Normal is just a cycle on the washing machine.
—WHOOPI GOLDBERG

The question is not whether our ideas are crazy, but whether they are crazy enough.
—KOBI YAMADA

WHAT'S
NEXT

WE GROW IN TIME TO TRUST THE FUTURE FOR OUR ANSWERS.

—RUTH BENEDICT

There can be no progress unless people have faith in tomorrow.

—JOHN F. KENNEDY

Never sell tomorrow short. There's plenty to get excited about. Be filled with expectation, hope and confidence. Believe something good is going to happen—and it usually will.

—DR. ROBERT SCHULLER

WHAT'S NEXT

The secret to a rich life is to have more beginnings than endings.

—DAVE WEINBAUM

I like the dreams of the future better than the history of the past.

—THOMAS JEFFERSON

Entrepreneurs share a faith in a bright future. They have a clear vision of where they are going and what they are doing, and they have a pressing need to succeed.

—RONALD REAGAN

There are things known and there are things unknown, and in between are the doors.

—JIM MORRISON

As long as you're worrying about losing what you've got, you'll never be able to see that what's out there waiting for you is a hundred times better!

—DON WARD

There are far far better things ahead than any we leave behind.

—C. S. LEWIS

WHAT'S
NEXT

JUST REMEMBER— WHEN YOU THINK ALL IS LOST, THE FUTURE REMAINS.

—BOB GODDARD

It's never too late—in fiction or in life—to revise.
—NANCY THAYER

Man is a creature of hope and invention,
both of which belie the idea that things cannot
be changed.
—TOM CLANCY

If things look hopeless, look and see if you aren't
facing the wrong direction.
—JAMES EVERETT

WHAT'S
NEXT

The need for change bulldozed a road down the center of my mind.
—MAYA ANGELOU

The past cannot be changed. The future is yet in your power.
—MARY PICKFORD

The best part of human history lies in the future, not in the past.
—BERTRAND RUSSELL

If you don't like what you're doing, you can always pick up your needle and move to another groove.
—TIMOTHY LEARY

Beyond each corner new directions lie in wait.
—STANISLAW JERZY LEE

My life now, my whole life apart from anything that can happen to me, every minute of it has the positive meaning of goodness which I still have the power to put into it.
—KONSTANTINE LEVIN IN "ANNA KARENINA"

WHAT'S NEXT

Your past is not your potential. In any hour
you can liberate the future.
—MARILYN FERGUSON

The essence of optimism is that it takes no account
of the present, but it is a source of inspiration, of
vitality and hope where others have resigned; it
enables us to hold our heads high, to claim the
future for ourselves and not to abandon it.
—DIETRICH BONHOEFFER

As long as you can start, you are all right.
The juice will come.
—ERNEST HEMINGWAY

Tomorrow is always fresh, with no mistakes in it.
—LUCY MAUD MONTGOMERY

When you are inspired by some great purpose, some extraordinary project, all your thoughts break their bonds; your mind transcends limitations; your consciousness expands in every direction; and you find yourself in a great, new and wonderful world.
—PATANJALI

Overcoming our fear of the unexpected and discovering the unknown is what ignites our spirit. It is what life is all about.
—DANIEL S. GOLDIN

WHAT'S
NEXT

WHEN YOU'RE THROUGH LEARNING, YOU'RE THROUGH.

—VERNON LAW

In a time of drastic change it is the learners who inherit the future. The learned usually find themselves equipped to live in a world that no longer exists.

—ERIC HOFFER

The faster you learn, the bigger you win.

—JIM HAUDAN

In today's rapidly changing world it's not our know-how, it's our learn-how that ensures our continued success in business and in life.

—LARRY WILSON

WHAT'S
NEXT

Learning is what most adults will do for a living in the 21st century.

—UNKNOWN

The illiterate of the future are not those who cannot read or write. They are those who cannot learn, unlearn, and relearn.

—ALVIN TOFFLER

Original ideas come from reassembling knowledge in new ways. But you need to have that knowledge in your mind before you can reassemble it.

—LEON BOTSTEIN

Learning is discovering that something is possible.
—FRITZ PERLS

And when you have reached the mountain top,
then you shall begin to climb.
—KAHLIL GIBRAN

Each destination you reach only opens out into
wider horizons, new and undiscovered countries
for you to explore.
—BARBARA SHER

WHAT'S
NEXT

LEADERS TODAY MUST BE EVANGELISTS FOR CHANGING THE SYSTEM— NOT FOR PRESERVING IT.

—JOHNATHAN BULKELEY, CEO,
   BARNES & NOBLE

Leadership today is less about what we know
and more about what we're willing to discover.

—DIANE BRANSON

The leader should have the spirit of adventure—
the pioneer spirit which blazes new trails.

—MARY PARKER FOLLETT

The best leaders are not interested in selling
their own ideas, but in finding the best ideas.
They are not interested in having their own way,
but in finding the best way.

—DAN ZADRA

WHAT'S
NEXT

There are no limits on our future if we don't put limits on our people.

—JACK KEMP

Creative ideas reside in people's minds but are trapped by fear or rejection. Create a judgment-free environment on the inside and you'll unleash a torrent of creativity on the outside.

—ALEX OSBORNE

New ideas are not born in a conforming environment.

—ROGER VON OECH

I have a great belief in the fact that whenever there is chaos, it creates wonderful thinking. I consider chaos a gift.

—SEPTIMA POINSETTA CLARK

One of the benefits of being disorderly is that you are constantly making exciting discoveries.

—A.A. MILNE

Just get it down on paper, and then we'll see what to do with it.

—MAXWELL EVARTS PERKINS

WHAT'S
NEXT

EVEN LAST MONTH'S MANUAL SHOULD BE OUT OF DATE.

—TAIICHI OHNO, TOYOTA

Today's shocks are tomorrow's conventions.
—CAROLYN HEILBRUN

Imagine a school with children who can read
and write, but with teachers who cannot, and
you have a metaphor of the Information Age in
which we live.
—PETER COCHRANE

We are now at a point where we must educate
our children in what no one knew yesterday, and
prepare our schools for what no one knows yet.
—MARGARET MEAD

WHAT'S
NEXT

This is your wake-up call: The new economy operates 24 hours a day, 7 days a week.

—ANNA MUOIO, "FAST COMPANY"

The biggest challenge facing companies in the 21st century will be to differentiate themselves from everyone else—to create a passionate following among customers who have too many choices.

—ANDY & KATE SPADE, COFOUNDERS, KATE SPADE

The individual is forcing the change. People are shopping around, not only for the right products, but for the right job. They now regard the old rules of business as dishonest, boring, and outdated.

—ANITA RODDICK, THE BODY SHOP

American businesses with few exceptions—
Merck, Intel, and Citibank come to mind—still
seem to think that innovation is a "flash of
genius," when it should be a systematic,
organized, rigorous discipline.

—PETER DRUCKER

What we have done has barely scratched the
surface. It turns out that there is, in fact, unlimited
juice in that lemon. The fact is, this is not about
squeezing anything at all: It is about tapping an
ocean of creativity, passion, and energy.

—JACK WELCH

WHAT'S
NEXT

CHANGE IS INEVITABLE, GROWTH IS INTENTIONAL.

—GLENDA CLOUD

Going from—toward; it is the history of every
one of us.

—HENRY DAVID THOREAU

Nobody gets to live life backwards.
Look ahead, that is where your future lies.

—ANN LANDERS

I embrace emerging experience. I participate in
discovery. I am a butterfly. I am not a butterfly
collector. I want the experience of a butterfly.

—SIR EDWARD WILLIAM STAFFORD

WHAT'S
NEXT

A permanent state of transition is man's most noble condition.

—JUAN RAMÓN JIMÉNEZ

In life, change is inevitable. In business, change is vital.

—WARREN BENNIS

We have learned to love change.
I will go anywhere to talk to people who say they are doing things in a better way.

—ANITA RODDICK, THE BODY SHOP

Human beings, by change, renew, rejuvenate ourselves; otherwise we harden.

—JOHANN VON GOETHE

He allowed himself to be swayed by his conviction that human beings are not born once and for all on the day their mothers give birth to them, but that life obliges them over and over again to give birth to themselves.

—GABRIEL GARCIA MARQUEZ

I've got my faults, but living in the past is not one of them. There's no future in it.

—SPARKY ANDERSON

WHAT'S
NEXT

IN A MOVING WORLD, READAPTATION IS THE PRICE OF LONGEVITY.

—GEORGE SANTAYANA

Part of the economy dies every day and is replaced by something new.
—PAUL HAWKEN

Of America's largest companies at the beginning of the 20th century, only 16 are still in business.
—"ACROSS THE BOARD" MAGAZINE

The times, they are a-changin'. The slow one now will later be fast. And the first one now will later be last.
—BOB DYLAN

It is not the strongest of the species that survive, nor even the most intelligent, but the one most responsive to change.
—CHARLES DARWIN

We don't remain good if we don't always strive to become better.
—GOTTFRIED KELLER

The only sustainable competitive advantage is the ability to learn faster than the competition.
—ARIE DE GEUS

Your biggest competitor is your own view
of your future.

—WATTS WACKER & JIM TAYLOR

The ones who make it see the difference
between what is and what can be.

—KOBI YAMADA

A competitive world offers two possibilities.
You can lose. Or, if you want to win, you
can change.

—L. C. THUROW

WHAT'S
NEXT

DWELL COMFORTABLY IN THE MIDST OF PROFOUND UNCERTAINTY.

—JOHN KEATS

The only person who likes change is a wet baby.
—ROGER VON OECH

The future is like heaven—everyone exalts it but no one wants to go there now.
—JAMES BALDWIN

Our dilemma is that we hate change, but we love it at the same time. What we want is for things to remain the same but get better.
—SYDNEY J. HARRIS

WHAT'S
NEXT

Be delighted that the future is unsure.
That's the way it should be.
—UNKNOWN

Change is the constant, the signal for rebirth,
the egg of the phoenix.
—CHRISTINA BALDWIN

Everything in the universe is subject to change
and everything is right on schedule.
—ANONYMOUS

Leave your comfort zone. Go stretch yourself for a good cause.

—KOBI YAMADA

Living is a form of not being sure, not knowing what's next or how. The moment we know how, we begin to die a little. We never entirely know. We guess. We may be wrong, but we take leap after leap in the dark.

—AGNES DE MILLE

Whatever you are meant to do, move toward it and it will come to you.

—GLORIA DUNN

WHAT'S
NEXT

WHILE WE ARE POSTPONING, LIFE SPEEDS BY.

—SENECA

Might, could, would—they are contemptible auxiliaries.

—GEORGE ELIOT

It had long since come to my attention that people of accomplishment rarely sat back and let things happen to them. They went out and happened to things.

—ELINOR SMITH

The window of opportunity doesn't stay open for very long. That's why as soon as we've defined a compelling product, we devote all of our energies to blasting through that window.

—BILL HUNT, RAZA FOUNDRIES, INC.

WHAT'S
NEXT

Leaders make decisions that create the future they desire.

—MIKE MURDOCK

Wherever you see a successful business, someone once made a courageous decision.

—PETER DRUCKER

I do what I love. You don't need an MBA to be successful. You need a unique concept and guts.

—DEBORAH KARABIN

Envisioning the end is enough to put the means in motion.

—DOROTHEA BRANDE

Understand there are no guarantees, make a bet on your future, and then throw everything you got into it.

—CATHY LARSON

Act boldly and unseen forces will come to your aid.

—DOROTHEA BRANDE

WHAT'S
NEXT

THE FUTURE HAS A WAY OF ARRIVING UNANNOUNCED.

—GEORGE F. WILL

The executive of the future will be rated by his ability to anticipate his problems rather than to meet them as they come.
—HOWARD COONLEY

Intelligence recognizes what has happened. Genius recognizes what will happen.
—JOHN CIARDI

What we anticipate seldom occurs; what we least expected generally happens.
—BENJAMIN DISRAELI

WHAT'S
NEXT

The world is never in a state of fixation,
but is always changing; we are not looking at
a lantern-slide but at a moving picture.
—ANDREW LLOYD JAMES

In the next twenty years, the commerce
of ideas is going to become more important
than the commerce of things.
—DOUGLAS VAN HOUWELING

The factory of the future will have only two
employees, a man and a dog. The man will be
there to feed the dog. The dog will be there to
keep the man from touching the equipment.
—WARREN BENNIS

Technology evolves so much faster than wisdom.
—JENNIFER STONE

Technical knowledge today has the shelf life
of fruit.
—MIKE RUETTGERS

We'll get computers that are a million times faster
over the next 10 years. The key message here is
that we are just at the beginning of the revolution—
today's machines are Model T's.
—BILL GATES

WHAT'S
NEXT

THE REALITY IS THAT CHANGES ARE COMING. THEY MUST COME. WE MUST ALL SHARE IN BRINGING THEM.

—JOHN HERSEY

Reorganization is the permanent condition of a healthy organization.

—ROY ASH

I am convinced that if the rate of change inside an organization is less than the rate of change outside, the end is in sight.

—JACK WELCH

The world is advancing, and an organization must be willing to change and improve. The only sacred cow in an organization is its principles.

—BUCK RODGERS

WHAT'S
NEXT

So much has been written about employees' resistance to change that we are sometimes tempted to forget that they can also react favorably.

—NATHANIEL STEWART

I see people who can't wait to get to work to see what's going to happen next.

—TOM PICKETT

Small companies especially are a hotbed of innovation. Small firms produce 24 times as many innovations per R&D dollar as the largest firms.

—NATIONAL SCIENCE FOUNDATION

People don't resist change, they resist being changed.

—PETER SCHOLTES

Smart organizations of the future won't try to manage change processes. Instead they will nurture the spirit of change within their people. That way, change will occur naturally, and it will preserve the heart and soul of the organization.

—SUE SIMMONS

As long as people can change, the world can change.

—UNKNOWN

WHAT'S
NEXT

WHEN YOU WISH UPON A START…

—UNKNOWN

The moment of change is the only poem.

—ADRIENNE RICH

We believe it is a necessity of our times to translate our beliefs, our hopes and ideals into concrete action.

—LENEDRA CAROLL

Thunder is fine, thunder is impressive; but it is lightning that does the work.

—MARK TWAIN

WHAT'S
NEXT

They always say that time changes things,
but you actually have to change them yourself.

—ANDY WARHOL

If nothing changes—nothing changes.

—JIM WESTLEY

Ideas have a short shelf life. You must
act on them before the expiration date.

—JOHN C. MAXWELL

It doesn't matter how new an idea is:
what matters is how new it becomes.
—ELIAS CANETTI

Anybody can come up with new ideas.
Innovators make them happen.
—MICHAEL LEBOEUF

There is only one definition. An entrepreneur
is someone who gets something new done.
—PETER DRUCKER

WHAT'S
NEXT

THE FUTURE IS SIMPLY INFINITE POSSIBILITY WAITING TO HAPPEN. WHAT IT WAITS ON IS HUMAN IMAGINATION TO CRYSTALLIZE ITS POSSIBILITY.

—LELAND KAISER

We are the echoes of the future.

—WILLIAM MERWIN

We are tomorrow's past.

—MARY WEBB

We are at the very beginning of time for the
human race. It is not unreasonable that we
grapple with problems. But there are tens
of thousands of years in the future. Our
responsibility is to do what we can, learn what
we can, improve the solutions, and pass them on.

—RICHARD P. FEYNMAN

WHAT'S
NEXT

History isn't just the past. It's alive in us.
—NATALIE PORTMAN

Others have been here before me, and I walk in their footsteps. The books I have read were composed by generations of fathers and sons, mothers and daughters, teachers and disciples. I am the sum total of their experiences, their quests. And so are you.
—ELIE WIESEL

We look backward when we hear the term history. But history is about what is emerging and can emerge, as well as what has already emerged.

—MATTHEW FOX

We forget that we ourselves are a part of history, that we are the product of growth and are condemned to perish if we lose the capacity for further growth and change. We are ourselves history and share the responsibility for world history and our position in it.

—HERMAN HESSE

WHAT'S
NEXT

I HONOR THE HUMAN RACE. WHEN IT FACES LIFE HEAD-ON, IT CAN ALMOST REMAKE ITSELF.

—ELEANOR ROOSEVELT

The future is in the hands of those who can give tomorrow's generations valid reasons to live and hope.

—TEILHARD DE CHARDIN

The problems of the world cannot possibly be solved by skeptics or cynics whose horizons are limited by the obvious realities. We need men and women who can dream of things that never were.

—JOHN F. KENNEDY

Our children will create a world we cannot imagine; they will accomplish things we cannot even dream.

—KATHRYN T. SHAW

WHAT'S
NEXT

So many dreams are waiting to be realized.
—UNKNOWN

The most important discoveries will provide answers to questions that we do not yet know how to ask and will concern objects we have not yet imagined.
—JOHN N. BAHCALL

I haven't a clue how my story will end, but that's all right. When you set out on a journey and night covers the road, that's when you discover the stars.
—NANCY WILLARD